Test Bank

to accompany

Checkett/Checkett

The Write Start
Paragraphs to Essays

Prepared by

Timothy J. Florschuetz
Mesa Community College

Longman

New York Boston San Francisco
London Toronto Sydney Tokyo Singapore Madrid
Mexico City Munich Paris Cape Town Hong Kong Montreal

Test Bank to accompany Checkett/Checkett, *The Write Start: Paragraphs to Essays*

Copyright ©2002 Pearson Education, Inc.

Please visit our website at http://www.ablongman.com

ISBN: 0-321-06121-7

1 2 3 4 5 6 7 8 9 10 -VG- 04 03 02 01

Contents

Name_____   Instructor_____

Date_____   Score_____

Instructor Comments_____

Test A   Chapter 3   **The Introductory Paragraph**

For each of the following items, choose the best answer.

1.   An introductory paragraph consists of
        a.   complete sentences.
        b.   a thesis sentence.
        c.   a series of introductory sentences.
        d.   both a and b.
        e.   both b and c.

2.   The thesis sentence usually appears
        a.   at the beginning of the introductory paragraph.
        b.   at the end of the introductory paragraph.
        c.   anywhere in the introductory paragraph.

3.   The thesis sentence
        a.   has only one topic, never more.
        b.   does not express topic as a fact.
        c.   can outline the organizational structure of the essay.
        d.   all of the above.

4.   The controlling idea or attitude in a thesis sentence
        a.   has only one topic, never more.
        b.   does not express topic as a fact.
        c.   can outline the organizational structure of the essay.
        d.   all of the above.

5.   The verb usually starts to express your _____ about the topic.
        a.   attitude
        b.   opinion
        c.   facts
        d.   feelings

6.   The three-item essay map includes
        a.   an introductory paragraph, one body paragraph, and one concluding paragraph.
        b.   an introductory paragraph, three body paragraphs, and one concluding paragraph.
        c.   a thesis paragraph, two body paragraphs, and one concluding paragraph.

7. The three-item essay map lists _____ topics that will support your thesis.
   a. four
   b. two
   c. three

8. The purpose of an introductory sentence is to
   a. catch the reader's attention and clarify the author's tone.
   b. introduce the main topic and the author's opinion.
   c. start the essay with a thesis.

9. Some effective techniques for introducing a thesis sentence include
   a. using a shocking statistic or statement.
   b. stating a common problem or misconception.
   c. posing a series of questions.
   d. all of the above.

10. The thesis sentence has three elements:
    a. the topic, the controlling idea/attitude, and the tone.
    b. the topic, the controlling idea/attitude, and the essay map.
    c. the topic, the controlling idea/attitude, and the main idea.

Test B   Chapter 3   **The Introductory Paragraph**

For each of the following items, choose the correct answer.

1.   The thesis sentence is the most important element in any essay.
        a.   True
        b.   False

2.   The thesis sentence does not limit the scope of the essay.
        a.   True
        b.   False

3.   Words like is/is not and should/should not are examples of verbs that begin to tell the
        reader how the author feels about the topic.
        a.   True
        b.   False

4.   A clearly defined controlling idea/attitude helps the reader understand the focus of the
        essay after reading the body paragraphs.
        a.   True
        b.   False

5.   Professional essays are always five paragraphs.
        a.   True
        b.   False

6.   Parody is an example of tone.
        a.   True
        b.   False

7.   The thesis sentence expresses the topic as a question.
        a.   True
        b.   False

8.   The following sentence is an example of a proper thesis sentence:
        Octopi can change many colors, but they become red when angry.
        a.   True
        b.   False

9.   The thesis sentence from question 8 expresses the topic as a fact.
        a.   True
        b.   False

10. The thesis sentence is an example of a three-item essay map:
Everyone should carpool because it saves gas and decreases pollution.
   a. True
   b. False

Name_____   Instructor_____

Date_____   Score_____

Instructor Comments_____

Test A   Chapter 4   The Body Paragraphs

For each of the following items, choose the best answer.

1. The purpose of the body paragraphs of an essay is to _____ the topic stated in the thesis sentence in the introductory paragraph.
    a. develop
    b. support
    c. explain
    d. all of the above

2. The topic is the _____ of the body paragraph.
    a. subject
    b. controlling idea
    c. thesis

3. Support sentences help develop the subject by using
    a. specific facts, examples, and tone.
    b. specific facts, statistics, and details.
    c. specific facts, details, and examples.

4. The six reporter's questions are who, what, where, which, why, and how.
    a. True
    b. False

5. Writing your topic, controlling idea/attitude, and support ideas in a ladder-like list is called
    a. brainstorming.
    b. a working outline.
    c. a sketch.

6. The six reporter's questions provide focus and details for the body paragraphs.
    a. True
    b. False

7. The supporting ideas don't need to be consistent with the controlling idea or attitude.
    a. True
    b. False

8. The controlling idea/attitude allows new subjects or ideas to be introduced.
    a. True
    b. False

9.   A working outline is used to
      a.   discover whether or not you have a good working essay map.
      b.   discover whether or not you have a topic, controlling idea/attitude, and support.
      c.   discover whether or not you have good organization.

10.   The six reporter's questions are the only questions you should ask to make the paper focused.
      a.   True
      b.   False

Test B   **Chapter 4**   **The Body Paragraphs**

For each of the following pairs of sentences, correctly identify the support (S) and topic (T) sentence.

1.   _____ In a class, the teacher can influence a passion for learning.

      _____ Adding humor to the lecture will create a rapport with students.

2.   _____ For example, outdoor grilling is one of the great American neighborhood traditions.

      _____ Americans pride themselves on many great traditions.

3.   _____ One type of personality disorder is bipolar disorder.

      _____ Personality disorders can take many different forms.

4.   _____ Cats are now replacing dogs as humankind's best friend.

      _____ A popular choice of breed is the Siamese.

5.   _____ The newspaper contains valuable information on business, entertainment, sports, as well as politics and current events.

      _____ Less than 10% of the public read the newspaper.

Test A   Chapter 5   The Concluding Paragraph

For each of the following items, choose the best answer.

1.   A concluding paragraph
    a.   brings a sense of completion to the essay.
    b.   brings a sense of completion to the essay and restates the central thesis.
    c.   brings a sense of completion to the essay and re-emphasises the central thesis.

2.   The concluding paragraph is sometimes used to develop new points.
    a.   True
    b.   False

3.   In longer essays, restating the thesis in the concluding paragraph can be helpful to the reader.
    a.   True
    b.   False

4.   What are some of the techniques used in a concluding paragraph?

    _____   _____   _____   _____

5.   To do something based on the essay's content is
    a.   a warning.
    b.   a call to action.
    c.   a prediction.
    d.   an evaluation

6.   Summarizing and judging in a concluding paragraph is
    a.   an evaluation
    b.   a warning.
    c.   a prediction.
    d.   none of the above.

7.   In a concluding paragraph, the technique of looking into the future is called _____.
    a.   clairvoyance
    b.   prediction
    c.   warning
    d.   speculation

8. It is not necessary to have a concluding paragraph if the essay is extremely short.
   a. True
   b. False

9. The techniques in a concluding paragraph are to place emphasis on the points made throughout the essay.
   a. True
   b. False

10. Telling the reader about negative events to come and what to do about them is a _____.
    a. speculation
    b. call to action
    c. warning
    d. prediction

Test B   Chapter 5   The Concluding Paragraph

Choose the correct answer for each of the following sentences.

1.   Make sure the gas gauge does not fall below the E in a full injection car.
      a.   prediction
      b.   warning
      c.   call to action
      d.   evaluation

2.   Call or write to the March of Dimes, and suggest they use more funding to help provide better prenatal care for pregnant women.
      a.   prediction
      b.   warning
      c.   call to action
      d.   evaluation

3.   With the large number of job layoffs, bankruptcies will be on the rise over the next year.
      a.   prediction
      b.   warning
      c.   call to action
      d.   evaluation

4.   New medical treatments can be created from stem cell research, regardless of where the stem cells are derived.
      a.   prediction
      b.   warning
      c.   call to action
      d.   evaluation

5.   The college experience provides character building qualities like discipline, perseverance, and critical thinking skills.
      a.   prediction
      b.   warning
      c.   call to action
      d.   evaluation

6.   If it sounds too good to be true, it probably is.
      a.   prediction
      b.   warning
      c.   call to action
      d.   evaluation

7.   When you have a bad restaurant experience, ask for the manager.
      a.   prediction
      b.   warning
      c.   call to action
      d.   evaluation

8.   With 4% inflation, a loaf of bread that costs $1.25 will be $16.25 in 30 years.
      a.   prediction
      b.   warning
      c.   call to action
      d.   evaluation

9.   Make certain to read the fine print on any contract you sign.
      a.   prediction
      b.   warning
      c.   call to action
      d.   evaluation

10.   Set some money aside as soon as possible, and begin investing for the future.
      a.   prediction
      b.   warning
      c.   call to action
      d.   evaluation

Test A   Chapter 6   Prewriting Activities

For each of the following items, choose the correct answer.

1.   Getting started is the easiest part of writing.
        a.   True
        b.   False

2.   Four strategies to help a writer get started are listing, clustering, cubing, and mapping.
        a.   True
        b.   False

3.   Writing down any idea that comes to mind without thinking about it is called "free association."
        a.   True
        b.   False

4.   Clustering is similar to listing, but uses visual relationships to help see ideas more clearly.
        a.   True
        b.   False

5.   There is one strategy that is better than another.
        a.   True
        b.   False

6.   A six-sided perspective is called cubing.
        a.   True
        b.   False

7.   Cross-examination strategy should only be done with a partner.
        a.   True
        b.   False

8.   The goal of prewriting is discovery.
        a.   True
        b.   False

9.   Clustering is the same as mapping.
        a.   True
        b.   False

10. Cross-examination is a variation of the six reporter's questions.
    a. True
    b. False

Test B   Chapter 6   **Prewriting Activities**

Choose the correct answer for each of the following sentences.

1.   When doing the listing strategy you should _____ for at least 10 minutes.
      a.   use a computer
      b.   use the free association technique
      c.   think and brainstorm

2.   After listing ideas, arrange them into groups and find a logical order according to
      a.   priority.
      b.   importance.
      c.   chronology.
      d.   any of the above.

3.   The first step in the mapping technique is to
      a.   draw a circle and write the topic inside it.
      b.   brainstorm ideas and choose one.
      c.   draw a cube and write the topic inside it.

4.   Related topics circled in layers is part of the _____ techniques.
      a.   mapping
      b.   listing
      c.   clustering
      d.   a and c
      e.   b and c

5.   Which of the following are included in the six perspectives of the cubing strategy?
      a.   Free associate about the topic.
      b.   Apply the topic.
      c.   Organize the topic.
      d.   a and c
      e.   a and b

6.   Which of the following are included in the cross-examination technique?
      a.   testimony
      b.   description
      c.   a and b
      d.   none of the above

7.   The question "Is the subject impossible?" is an example of circumstance in
     a.   listing.
     b.   mapping.
     c.   cubing.
     d.   cross-examination.
     e.   any of the above techniques.

8.   When writing about a controversial subject like politics or religion, you may want to use
     the _____ as a guideline.
     a.   listing technique
     b.   mapping technique
     c.   cubing technique
     d.   cross-examination
     e.   any of the above techniques

9.   "How can the topic be used?" is an example of the _____ perspective in the
     cubing technique.
     a.   free associate about the topic
     b.   apply the topic
     c.   describe the topic

10. Each of the strategies should be done for at least _____ minutes.
     a.   15
     b.   10
     c.   5
     d.   8

Instructor Comments_____

Test A   Chapter 7   The Descriptive Essay

For each of the following items, choose the best answer.

1.   Effective description creates images in the reader's mind by using
      a.   specific details.
      b.   irony.
      c.   abstract language.
      d.   complex analysis.

2.   Description can be used to clarify, explain, or create a particular mood about a person, place, or thing.
      a.   True
      b.   False

3.   The two different types of description are
      a.   objective and illustrative.
      b.   illustrative and emotional.
      c.   objective and subjective.
      d.   emotional and subjective.

4.   _____ description relies on factual detail.
      a.   Objective
      b.   Illustrative
      c.   Emotional
      d.   Subjective

5.   _____ description creates an emotional feeling or impression.
      a.   Objective
      b.   Illustrative
      c.   Emotional
      d.   Subjective

6.   In a concluding paragraph for a descriptive essay, _____ is often used as the approach.
      a.   dominant impression
      b.   symbolism
      c.   evaluation
      d.   none of the above

7. In the introductory paragraph of a descriptive essay, the _____ is the controlling idea or attitude to the topic as a whole.
   a. dynamic impression
   b. symbolism
   c. evaluation
   d. none of the above

8. Focusing on more than one dominant impression, when writing descriptively, can make your writing clearer and more enjoyable.
   a. True
   b. False

9. When writing descriptively, it is unnecessary to provide sensory images for the reader.
   a. True
   b. False

10. Figurative language helps writers provide _____ in new and unique ways.
   a. similes
   b. complexities
   c. contrasts
   d. comparisons

Instructor Comments_____

Test B   **Chapter 7**   **The Descriptive Essay**

For each of the following prompts, create a thesis sentence which announces the topic, the writer's controlling attitude (dominant impression), and the essay map.

1.   A ghost town.

_____

_____

_____

_____

2.   A teacher.

_____

_____

_____

_____

3.   A circus.

_____

_____

_____

_____

4.   A painting.

_____

_____

_____

_____

5.   A dirty kitchen.

_____

_____

_____

_____

6.   A grandparent.

_____

_____

_____

_____

7.   A backyard.

_____

_____

_____

_____

8.   A family pet.

_____

_____

_____

_____

9.   A wild animal.

_____

_____

_____

_____

10.   A good friend.

_____

_____

_____

_____

Instructor Comments_____

Test A   Chapter 8   The Narrative Essay

For each of the following items, choose the best answer.

1.   Narration is different than telling an entertaining or informative story.
        a.   True
        b.   False

2.   Stories told through a narrative essay are always about an incident that actually happened.
        a.   True
        b.   False

3.   An effective narrative must have a point to the story and a reason why that story is important.
        a.   True
        b.   False

4.   Every narrative essay must have a clear
        a.   character sketch.
        b.   setting.
        c.   point or purpose.
        d.   none of the above.

5.   The easiest way to develop a narrative is to rely on the six reporter's questions: *who, what, where, when, why,* and *how.*
        a.   True
        b.   False

6.   The thesis in a narration essay should not blend into the rest of the introductory paragraph.
        a.   True
        b.   False

7.   While writing narratives, time and the sequence of events need to be illustrated through the proper use of transitional expressions.
        a.   True
        b.   False

8.   In a narrative essay, the thesis should
      a.   state the point of the story.
      b.   lay out the essay map.
      c.   both a and b
      d.   none of the above

9.   It is not necessary for a narrative or story to have a point to it.
      a.   True
      b.   False

10.   A narrative essay must contain a thesis sentence, an introduction, body paragraph, and a
      conclusion.
      a.   True
      b.   False

Test B   Chapter 8   The Narrative Essay

Write a narrative topic sentence for each of the following subjects. Be certain that the sentence expresses the point of the story. You will have to make up the point of each story.

1.   A favorite relative.

_____

_____

_____

_____

2.   An elementary school experience.

_____

_____

_____

_____

3.   An embarrassing moment.

_____

_____

_____

_____

4.   Visiting a museum.

_____

_____

_____

_____

5.   Meeting aliens from another planet.

_____

_____

_____

_____

6.   Losing a much-loved pet.

_____

_____

_____

_____

7.   Going out on a first date.

_____

_____

_____

_____

8.   A terrible restaurant.

_____

_____

_____

9.   An experience with weather.

_____

_____

_____

10.   Experiencing live music or theatre.

_____

_____

_____

_____

Test A   Chapter 9   The Example Essay

For each of the following items, choose the best answer.

1.   In an example essay, detailed examples are used to make a specific topic more general.
      a.   True
      b.   False

2.   All examples given in body paragraphs should support the _____ of the essay.
      a.   map
      b.   general topic
      c.   controlling idea
      d.   none of the above

3.   Transitional expressions are necessary to identify examples.
      a.   True
      b.   False

4.   The controlling idea is a statement that tells the reader what your _____ about your subject is.
      a.   thesis
      b.   essay map
      c.   attitude
      d.   none of the above

5.   Without transitional expressions, examples can simply appear as a list.
      a.   True
      b.   False

6.   Which of the following is not a good transition to use in an example essay?
      a.   for instance
      b.   to illustrate
      c.   specifically
      d.   generally

7.   The six reporter's questions have no relevance when writing an example essay.
      a.   True
      b.   False

8. The focus of the body paragraphs should be listed in the thesis sentence's essay map.
    a. True
    b. False

9. The thesis sentence should contain all of the following except
    a. the topic.
    b. the controlling idea.
    c. the word "example."
    d. the essay map.

10. Detailed examples in an example essay are developed in the _____ paragraph(s).
    a. introductory
    b. body
    c. conclusion

Test B   Chapter 9   The Example Essay

Create a three-item list of examples for each topic given.

1.   music   _____   _____   _____

2.   teachers   _____   _____   _____

3.   automobiles   _____   _____   _____

4.   movies   _____   _____   _____

5.   outdoor sports   _____   _____   _____

6.   indoor sports   _____   _____   _____

7.   books   _____   _____   _____

8.   advertisements   _____   _____   _____

9.   restaurants   _____   _____   _____

10.   families   _____   _____   _____

Test A   Chapter 10   The Classification Essay

For each of the following items, choose the best answer.

1.   The most important aspect of classification is to keep the classifying units the same.
     a.   True
     b.   False

2.   Classification can be described as breaking down a larger subject into groups of smaller, less complex sub-components.
     a.   True
     b.   False

3.   Classification is the process of breaking up categories into a complex topic.
     a.   True
     b.   False

4.   A classification essay thesis statement should contain
     a.   the writer's controlling idea.
     b.   the word *classification*.
     c.   the method of how the author picked the topic.
     d.   none of the above.

5.   A classification essay thesis statement should also contain
     a.   a statement about classification.
     b.   a statement about subsets.
     c.   an essay map containing the categories.
     d.   none of the above.

6.   New category paragraphs can be added into the essay even if they are not mentioned in the thesis statement.
     a.   True
     b.   False

7.   Transitional expressions help keep the categories from appearing as a list.
     a.   True
     b.   False

8. It is unnecessary to make a point with a classification essay.
   a. True
   b. False

9. If we were to classify instruments, which category or sub-unit does not apply to our method of division?
   a. wind instruments
   b. string instruments
   c. percussion instruments
   d. electric instruments

10. In a classification essay, each _____ paragraph expands on one of the categories.
    a. introductory
    b. topic
    c. transitional
    d. body

Name_____   Instructor_____

Date_____   Score_____

Instructor Comments_____

Test B   Chapter 10   The Classification Essay

For each of the following subjects, provide a controlling idea and three categories.

1.   Subject: Music
      Controlling Idea:_____
      Categories: 1._____
                  2._____
                  3._____

2.   Subject: Automobiles
      Controlling Idea:_____
      Categories: 1._____
                  2._____
                  3._____

3.   Subject: Pets
      Controlling Idea:_____
      Categories: 1._____
                  2._____
                  3._____

4.   Subject: Laws
      Controlling Idea:_____
      Categories: 1._____
                  2._____
                  3._____

5.   Subject: Bodies of Water
      Controlling Idea:_____
      Categories: 1._____
                  2._____
                  3._____

6.   Subject: Teachers
      Controlling Idea:_____
      Categories: 1._____
                  2._____
                  3._____

7.   Subject: Sports
       Controlling Idea: _____
       Categories: 1._____
                2._____
                3._____

8.   Subject: Restaurants
       Controlling Idea:_____
       Categories: 1._____
                 2._____
                3._____

9.   Television Shows
       Controlling Idea:_____
       Categories: 1._____
                 2._____
                3._____

10.   Subject: Books
       Controlling Idea:_____
       Categories: 1._____
                 2._____
                3._____

Test A   Chapter 11   The Process Essay

For each of the following items, choose the best answer.

1.   A process essay explains the steps necessary to complete
       a.   a procedure.
       b.   an operation.
       c.   an event.
       d.   all of the above.

2.   A process essay could be used effectively to explain the differences between cell mitosis and cell meiosis.
       a.   True
       b.   False

3.   A process essay could be used effectively to explain how cell mitosis and cell meiosis work.
       a.   True
       b.   False

4.   The two types of process essays are
       a.   informational and substantial.
       b.   directional and substantial.
       c.   substantial and insubstantial.
       d.   directional and informational.

5.   Which type of process essay explains to the reader how to do something?
       a.   informational process
       b.   directional process
       c.   substantial process
       d.   insubstantial process

6.   Which type of process essay explains to the reader how something was made, how an event occurred, or how something works?
       a.   informational process
       b.   directional process
       c.   substantial process
       d.   insubstantial process

7.   Both types of process essays are developed according to the order in which the steps of the process occurred.
     a.   True
     b.   False

8.   When writing process essays, we usually follow what is called chronological order.
     a.   True
     b.   False

9.   Unlike other types of essays, process essays do not rely on transitional expressions.
     a.   True
     b.   False

10. Directional and informational process essays should begin with a thesis statement that
     a.   announces the topic.
     b.   expresses the writer's controlling idea.
     c.   contains an essay map.
     d.   all of the above.

Name_____   Instructor_____

Date_____   Score_____

Instructor Comments_____

Test B   Chapter 11   The Process Essay

For each of the following subjects, identify whether the topic suggests an instruction/process (I) or a directional process (D). Then compose an effective thesis statement.

1.   _____   How to effectively lose weight.

       _____

       _____

       _____

       _____

2.   _____   How music "soothes the soul."

       _____

       _____

       _____

       _____

3.   _____   How a computer works.

       _____

       _____

       _____

4.   _____   How to write a process essay.

       _____

       _____

       _____

       _____

5.   _____   How the United States government works.

       _____

       _____

       _____

Test A   **Chapter 12**   **The Comparison or Contrast Essay**

For each of the following items, choose the best answer.

1.   Comparison and contrast writing focuses on a discussion of an object, idea, or item in terms of how it relates to its own features.
        a.   True
        b.   False

2.   When we compare things, we look for similarities, and when we contrast things, we look for differences.
        a.   True
        b.   False

3.   A comparison and contrast thesis statement must contain
        a.   the items to be compared or contrasted.
        b.   the controlling idea or attitude.
        c.   the organizational structure.
        d.   all of the above.

4.   Which of the following organizational plans presents information about one item first, then refers to this information when discussing the second item?
        a.   block method
        b.   point-by-point method
        c.   series-by-series method
        d.   diagram method

5.   Which of the following organizational plans presents information about both items together, creating an ongoing series of comparisons and contrasts?
        a.   block method
        b.   point-by-point method
        c.   series-by-series method
        d.   diagram method

6.   For a concluding paragraph to a comparison and contrast essay, an _____ of the main point seems appropriate.
        a.   informative explanation
        b.   essential listing
        c.   evaluation
        d.   extended analysis

7. Listing similarities and differences of the subjects in question can help one to decide whether to compare or contrast the subjects based on the strength of the details.
   a. True
   b. False

8. Most comparison and contrast essays focus on both similarities and differences.
   a. True
   b. False

9. Which of the following pairs of items would be logical to compare or contrast?
   a. music and a popstar
   b. criminals and crimes
   c. a private business and public service business
   d. Halloween and a Halloween mask

10. Which of the following pairs of items would be illogical to compare or contrast?
    a. alternative fuel and gasoline
    b. an airplane and a train
    c. a desk-top computer and a lap-top computer
    d. a book and a novel

Test B   Chapter 12   The Comparison or Contrast Essay

Compose both a comparison and a contrast thesis statement for the following five pairs of listed items.

1.   Desk-top Computers/Lap-top Computers
       Comparison: _____
       _____
       _____
       Contrast: _____
       _____
       _____

2.   Reading a book/Watching television
       Comparison: _____
       _____
       _____
       Contrast: _____
       _____
       _____

3.   Renting a movie on video/Going out to a movie
       Comparison: _____
       _____
       _____
       Contrast: _____
       _____
       _____

4.   Dogs/Cats
       Comparison: _____
       _____
       _____
       Contrast: _____
       _____
       _____

5. Living in a small town/Living in a big city
    Comparison: _____
    _____
    _____

    Contrast: _____
    _____
    _____

Test A   **Chapter 13**   **The Definition Essay**

For each of the following items, choose the best answer.

1.   A _____ definition and _____ definition are the two major types of definition.
    a.   class, extended
    b.   simple, class
    c.   simple, extended
    d.   none of the above

2.   Definition by negation begins by stating what a word or term
    a.   opposes.
    b.   demonstrates.
    c.   is not.
    d.   none of the above

3.   A definition essay does not incorporate other rhetorical modes of development.
    a.   True
    b.   False

4.   A dictionary definition is an example of _____ definition.
    a.   concrete
    b.   abstract
    c.   simple
    d.   extended

5.   In a definition essay, the thesis statement should
    a.   state the topic to be defined.
    b.   state an attitude toward the topic.
    c.   stress the main points that will be made.
    d.   all of the above

6.   The thesis statement will also suggest the rhetorical mode of development.
    a.   True
    b.   False

7.   The body paragraphs of a definition essay may vary in rhetorical mode.
    a.   True
    b.   False

8. Appropriate transitional expressions for developing a definition essay are unnecessary because definition writing uses any and all rhetorical modes of development.
    a. True
    b. False

9. The concluding paragraph for a definition essay should
    a. redefine the subject in new and unique terms.
    b. provide the dictionary definition.
    c. flow naturally from the essay's main topic.
    d. all of the above

10. All definition essays should include the dictionary definition.
    a. True
    b. False

Test B   Chapter 13   The Definition Essay

For each of the following terms, create a thesis statement that reflects the given mode of development.

1.   Hate (contrast)

_____
_____
_____

2.   Hate (exemplification)

_____
_____
_____

3.   Pride (comparison)

_____
_____
_____

4.   Pride (exemplification)

_____
_____
_____

5.   Space (comparison)

_____
_____
_____

6.   Space (exemplification)

_____
_____
_____

7.   Beauty (description)

_____
_____
_____

8. Beauty (contrast)

   _____

   _____

   _____

9. Terrorism (process)

   _____

   _____

   _____

10. Terrorism (description)

   _____

   _____

   _____

Test A   Chapter 14   The Cause or Effect Essay

For each of the following items, choose the best answer.

1.   Cause and effect essays analyze
        a.   special relationships.
        b.   casual relationships.
        c.   causal relationships.
        d.   hierarchical relationships.

2.   Developing a _____ before one begins writing will help one focus on the series
        of events and clarify the relationships between these events.
        a.   causal chain
        b.   great chain of being
        c.   casual chain
        d.   all of the above

3.   Chronological order and coincidence help to develop the true cause and effect
        relationships.
        a.   True
        b.   False

4.   The topic sentence for a cause and effect paragraph should clearly state that the paragraph
        will either focus on causes or effects.
        a.   True
        b.   False

5.   Which of the following transitional expressions does not suggest causes?
        a.   since
        b.   the reason
        c.   consequently
        d.   because

6.   Which of the following transitional expressions does not suggest effects?
        a.   as a result
        b.   as a consequence of
        c.   caused by
        d.   then

7. Cause analysis develops _____ something happens.
   a. when
   b. where
   c. why
   d. how

8. Effect analysis explains the _____ stemming from the causes.
   a. actions and lessons
   b. truth and consequences
   c. coincidences and chronological order
   d. results and consequences

9. In a cause or effect essay, the thesis statement should
   a. demonstrate order.
   b. indicate action.
   c. be causal and effective.
   d. none of the above

10. A cause and effect essay will normally develop either causes or effects.
    a. True
    b. False

Test B   Chapter 14   The Cause or Effect Essay

For each of the following terms, create a thesis statement that reflects the given mode of development.

1.   Drug abuse
       Cause_____
       _____
       _____
       _____

2.   Poverty
       Cause_____
       _____
       _____
       _____

3.   Racial Intolerance
       Cause_____
       _____
       _____
       _____

4.   Vegetarianism
       Cause_____
       _____
       _____
       _____

5.   Sex in Advertising
       Cause_____
       _____
       _____
       _____

Test A   Chapter 15   The Persuasive Essay

For each of the following items, choose the best answer.

1.   When we write a persuasive essay, we try to convince someone else that our view, opinion, or belief is the only option.
    a.   True
    b.   False

2.   When writing a persuasive essay, it is only necessary to know the major argumentative points concerning your side of the argument.
    a.   True
    b.   False

3.   Persuasion is the most common type of writing in college.
    a.   True
    b.   False

4.   Formal persuasion is normally called
    a.   argumentation.
    b.   research.
    c.   analysis.
    d.   logic.

5.   A thesis statement in a persuasion essay should contain the writer's conclusion or point of view concerning the topic.
    a.   True
    b.   False

6.   It is unnecessary to set up a list of pros and cons concerning a topic before writing a persuasive piece because it will become evident in the essay.
    a.   True
    b.   False

7.   Any rhetorical mode may be used as support.
    a.   True
    b.   False

8.	Which of the following are considered valid organizational plans for a persuasive paragraph? (Circle all that apply.)
	a.	using only support points that argue for your point of view
	b.	using only the opposition's points of view
	c.	arguing against the opposition's support points
	d.	alternating support points and listing opposition support points while arguing against them

9.	Which of the following is not considered a valid type of support used to convince readers?
	a.	predicting causes
	b.	answering the opposition
	c.	referring to authority
	d.	facts and examples

10.	Transitional expressions are as extremely important in persuasive writing as they are in other modes of development.
	a.	True
	b.	False

Test B   Chapter 15   The Persuasive Essay

For each of the following statements, identify the type of "false logic" illustrated: ad homonym, bandwagon, either-or, hasty generalization, non sequitur, or red herring.

1.   Are we going to do something about the federal income tax, or are we going to continue to lose a majority of our incomes?

   _____

2.   "All of my friends get to go to the party, so I should get to go, too," exclaimed Hutch.

   _____

3.   Everybody has cell phones, so I better get one.

   _____

4.   I better get my navel pierced to keep up with all of the cheerleaders.

   _____

5.   Bill Clinton's policies remind me of a snake-oil salesman's advertisements.

   _____

6.   Carlos is not doing well in school because his teachers do not recognize the fact that he works full time.

   _____

7.   Illegal immigrants should be allowed to work in the United States because they work harder than Americans.

   _____

8.   The bill sponsored by that committee is immoral. That committee's chair is having an affair.

   _____

9.   My boss is a slave-driver; she docks my pay if I am fifteen minutes late.

   _____

10. Our basketball team's players are all failing their classes because they spend too much time practicing.

   _____

Test A   Chapter 16   The Research Paper

For each of the following items, choose the best answer.

1.   The research paper can be considered as an extended essay.
      a.   True
      b.   False

2.   A research paper does not have to have documented sources for support.
      a.   True
      b.   False

3.   A thesis sentence with an essay map will
      a.   limit your subject.
      b.   clearly define the paper's organization.
      c.   state your attitude towards the topic.
      d.   all of the above

4.   You should be able to find a minimum of five to ten books, articles, and critical essays
      about your topic to support your views.
      a.   True
      b.   False

5.   You should have your thesis sentence finalized before researching and reading about your
      subject.
      a.   True
      b.   False

6.   It does not matter whether or not your source material comes from an objective source or
      a biased source.
      a.   True
      b.   False

7.   What kind of material should you look for to support your ideas and conclusions?
      a.   appeals to emotion
      b.   appeals to reason
      c.   appeals to the opposition
      d.   none of the above

8. Sub-topics for the research paper are developed in the body paragraphs.
   a. True
   b. False

9. All research papers must include a Works Cited page.
   a. True
   b. False

10. Failure to document the use of another's ideas, even if you put it in your words, is called _____.
    a. misquoting
    b. summarizing
    c. plagiarism
    d. none of the above

Test B   **Chapter 16**   **The Research Paper**

Place the following steps for the research paper writing process in the correct numerical sequence.

1. _____   Write the paper.

2. _____   Create the outline.

3. _____   Select the topic you know you can find information about.

4. _____   Research the topic and take notes.

5. _____   Prepare the paper for submission.

6. _____   Document the paper using the appropriate format.

7. _____   Limit the topic by stating the paper's purpose.

8. _____   Select the quotations and citations.

9. _____   Proofread the paper.

10. _____   Arrange the quotations and citations in the order they will be used in your paper.

Test A   Chapter 17   The Essay Exam

For each of the following items, choose the best answer.

1.   All essay exams should be treated equally in regards to how you prepare to answer the
     essay question.
     a.   True
     b.   False

2.   Timing is an essential factor for essay exam success.
     a.   True
     b.   False

3.   Essay questions are called
     a.   terms.
     b.   responses.
     c.   modes.
     d.   prompts.

4.   Key terms in the essay question will often tell you the kind of response the instructor is
     looking for.
     a.   True
     b.   False

5.   You should not use an essay map to plan your essay because there is not enough time.
     a.   True
     b.   False

6.   It is unnecessary to pace yourself during an essay exam.
     a.   True
     b.   False

7.   You should use the _____ to help you create a few interesting lead-in sentences in
     the introductory paragraph.
     a.   course title
     b.   topic sentence
     c.   essay prompt
     d.   none of the above

8.   You do not need an introduction or conclusion for your response to an essay question.
        a.   True
        b.   False

9.   Helping you figure out how to respond to the essay question is best illustrated by the
        a.   key term(s).
        b.   topic.
        c.   attitude.
        d.   none of the above

10.   Essay exams usually involve the challenge of relying on your memory for ideas and facts.
        a.   True
        b.   False

Test B   **Chapter 17**   **The Essay Exam**

Underline the key term or terms in each of the following essay prompts.

1.   Discuss the moral dilemma facing the proponents of capital punishment.

2.   Shakespeare, in his romantic comedies, treats courtly love and romantic love differently. Explain his approach and define these two types of love.

3.   Summarize the trends which eventually led to the Great Depression.

4.   In your view, what are the two primary causes of the Civil War?

5.   Compare and contrast nuclear fusion with nuclear fission.

6.   Evaluate the reasons for legalizing marijuana in the United States.

7.   Watch the following six television advertisements; then, classify them based on their persuasive techniques.

8.   Analyze the function of the mitochondria.

9.   Describe the major effects of the Internet on international trade.

10.   Many researchers have documented the effects of global warming. Discuss these effects and provide specific illustrations.

Test A   **Chapter 18**   **The Literary Analysis**

For each of the following items, choose the best answer.

1.   A work of criticism involves interpreting and evaluating your own work.
        a.   True
        b.   False

2.   A narrator tells us about the characters in the _____ method of development.
        a.   dramatic
        b.   statistic
        c.   expository
        d.   none of the above

3.   Cultural qualities of the setting include which of the following? (Circle all that apply.)
        a.   moral
        b.   community
        c.   social
        d.   political

4.   Generally, a theme should be a moral, a commandment, or a directive about how to live.
        a.   True
        b.   False

5.   When discussing theme, you should not discuss how the work affected you personally.
        a.   True
        b.   False

6.   Round characters remain essentially unchanged throughout the work.
        a.   True
        b.   False

7.   _____ introduces you to the universe of the work and to the characters and their interrelationships.
        a.   A Flashback
        b.   The Climax
        c.   Resolution
        d.   Exposition

8.   The point of view refers to who is telling the story.
     a.   True
     b.   False

9.   The information presented by a third person narrator is considered accurate and truthful.
     a.   True
     b.   False

10. The reporter's questions of who, what, where, when, why, and how are essential when analyzing literature.
     a.   True
     b.   False

Test B   **Chapter 18**   **The Literary Analysis**

For each of the following items, choose the best answer.

1.   A _____ is an object that has taken on abstract meaning and value.
    a.   metaphor
    b.   theme
    c.   symbol

2.   A statement in which one thing is used to explain another is _____.
    a.   a metaphor
    b.   an oxymoron
    c.   a denotation

3.   When animals, objects, or ideas are given human characteristics or emotions, we call it
    _____.
    a.   symbolism
    b.   personification
    c.   irony

4.   A _____.is similar to a metaphor but uses the word "like" or "as" in creating the
    relationship between two entities.
    a.   paradox
    b.   symbol
    c.   simile

5.   _____ creates a reality the opposite from what appears true.
    a.   Irony
    b.   Symbolism
    c.   Abstraction

6.   A statement that initially appears self-contradictory is called a _____.
    a.   connotation
    b.   paradox
    c.   symbol

7.   _____ language is the use of words in their accepted, dictionary-defined sense.
    a.   Connotative
    b.   Denotative
    c.   Abstract

8.   _____ language is the use of words which have associations and implications apart from their explicit sense.
     a.   Connotative
     b.   Denotative
     c.   Abstract

9.   _____ language is using words that refer to ideas or concepts that cannot be perceived.
     a.   Connotative
     b.   Denotative
     c.   Abstract

10. A thesis sentence for a literary analysis essay should include the author, genre, title, topic, and evaluation of the topic.
     a.   True
     b.   False

Instructor Comments_____

Quiz A   **The Writer's Resources: Nouns and Pronouns**

For each of the following items, choose the best answer.

1.   Nouns are words which stand for
      a.   actions.
      b.   descriptions.
      c.   things.
      d.   all of the above.

2.   Nouns are normally classified as
      a.   proper and improper nouns.
      b.   common and uncommon nouns.
      c.   proper and common nouns.
      d.   objective and subjective nouns.

3.   To form the plural of most nouns, we simply add an –s or –es to the end of the word.
      a.   True
      b.   False

4.   Some nouns do not change at all when forming the plural.
      a.   True
      b.   False

5.   The name *C. S. Lewis* is an example of
      a.   a common noun.
      b.   a subjective noun.
      c.   a proper noun.
      d.   none of the above

6.   The word *professor* is an example of
      a.   a common noun.
      b.   a subjective noun.
      c.   a proper noun.
      d.   none of the above

7.   A pronoun takes place of, or refers to, a noun.
      a.   True
      b.   False

8.   ____ nouns are general terms which are not capitalized.
    a.   Common
    b.   Subjective
    c.   Proper
    d.   Objective

9.   ____ nouns are specific names or titles and are always capitalized.
    a.   Common
    b.   Subjective
    c.   Proper
    d.   Objective

10.   Sentences can have more than one noun.
    a.   True
    b.   False

Quiz B   **The Writer's Resources: Nouns and Pronouns**

For each of the following items, choose the best answer.

1.   Pronouns take the place of, or refer to, ____
        a.   nouns.
        b.   common nouns.
        c.   proper nouns.
        d.   all of the above.

2.   A pronoun should refer to a known ____
        a.   relative word.
        b.   improper noun.
        c.   antecedent.
        d.   common noun.

3.   A ____ refers to any person.
        a.   personal pronoun
        b.   antecedent
        c.   relative noun
        d.   improper noun

4.   Subjective pronouns are used as ____ in sentences.
        a.   subjects
        b.   objects
        c.   possessives

5.   Objective pronouns are used as ____ in sentences.
        a.   subjects
        b.   objects
        c.   possessives

6.   ____ is a subjective pronoun, while ____ is an objective pronoun.
        a.   Me, my
        b.   Her, she
        c.   He, his

7.   Relative pronouns, such as *who, which,* and *that,* introduce a qualifying or explanatory clause.
        a.   True
        b.   False

8. Pronouns do not have to agree (singular or plural) with their antecedents.
   a. True
   b. False

9. *Anybody* is an example of what type of pronoun?
   a. demonstrative
   b. relative
   c. indefinite

10. Demonstrative pronouns are used to point out or specify certain people, places, or things.
    a. True
    b. False

Quiz C   **The Writer's Resources: Nouns and Pronouns**

Underline all nouns and pronouns in each sentence.

1.   Georgio and his brother walk to school daily.

2.   Each is required for passing the exam.

3.   Anybody who would like to arrive early is welcome.

4.   Maria gave the gift to her.

5.   His computer needs a new monitor.

6.   We owe it to ourselves.

7.   Who is coming over for dinner tonight?

8.   She gave it to him.

9.   That is why.

10.   You have to be happy with yourself before making others happy.

Instructor Comments_____

Quiz A   **The Writer's Resources: Verbs**

For each of the following items, choose the best answer.

1.   Verbs are words that indicate
    a.   feeling.
    b.   being.
    c.   action.
    d.   all of the above.

2.   Which of the following is not one of the three main classes of verbs?
    a.   action verbs
    b.   linking verbs
    c.   passive verbs
    d.   helping verbs

3.   Present, past, and future tenses (or time) are not indicated through verb forms.
    a.   True
    b.   False

4.   We form simple past tense with regular verbs by adding
    a.   *-es* or *-s.*
    b.   *-ied or -ed.*
    c.   *-ed or -d.*
    d.   all of the above

5.   Simple past tense refers to an action that began and ended at one time period in the past.
    a.   True
    b.   False

6.   Irregular verbs follow different patterns to show past tense.
    a.   True
    b.   False

7.   The words *am, are, was, where,* and *is* are all forms of the verb *be.*
    a.   True
    b.   False

8.   _____ illustrates a subject of a sentence being acted upon.
    a.   Active voice
    b.   Passive voice
    c.   Subjective voice

9.   _____ illustrates a subject of a sentence doing the acting.
    a.   Active voice
    b.   Passive voice
    c.   Subjective voice

10.   We use helping verbs to create verb agreement in English.
    a.   True
    b.   False

Quiz B   **The Writer's Resources: Verbs**

Underline all of the verbs in the following sentences.

1.   We climb mountains everyday during the summers in Colorado.

2.   I think; therefore, I am.

3.   Everyone will be skating at the frozen pond tomorrow night.

4.   Raylene has shopped for hours and hours.

5.   The car crashed into the barrier and slid off the road.

6.   My brother hates to clean the bathroom but loves to clean the garage.

7.   The shark bit the surfer.

8.   The surfer was bitten by the shark.

9.   For over six hours, Mikhail has been studying.

10.   Behind the barn lies a pile of bones.

Quiz C   **The Writer's Resources: Verbs**

For each of the following sentences, underline the correct verb form which agrees with the subject.

1.   Toni and I (go, goes) to work at six in the morning.

2.   Every Halloween, a crowd (come, comes) knocking at our front door.

3.   Either one of the dresses (look, looks) beautiful on you.

4.   Everybody (is, are) attending the concert at the park tonight.

5.   Wilma's sisters (bake, bakes) the best peanut butter cookies in the land.

6.   Either the cat or the dog (is, are) responsible for the mess in the kitchen.

7.   Either my brother or my sisters (is, are) going to have to repair the roof.

8.   The band (play, plays) two shows every afternoon.

9.   The box of earrings (has, have) been stolen.

10.   The chair facing Tisha and Omar (sit, sits) at an awkward angle.

Quiz A   **The Writer's Resources: Adjectives/Adverbs**

For each of the following items, choose the best answer.

1.   Adjectives modify
       a.   nouns.
       b.   pronouns.
       c.   proper nouns.
       d.   all of the above.
       e.   none of the above.

2.   Adverbs modify
       a.   adjectives.
       b.   nouns.
       c.   verbs.
       d.   a and c.
       e.   all of the above.

3.   Adjectives often end with the letters –ly.
       a.   True
       b.   False

4.   Adjectives usually come ____ the nouns they modify.
       a.   before
       b.   after

5.   Adverbs always come after the verbs they modify.
       a.   True
       b.   False

6.   The questions of *where, how,* or *when* can be answered by
       a.   adjectives.
       b.   adverbs.

7.   Adjectives are used to describe objective sensory details of nouns.
       a.   True
       b.   False

8.   The word *beautifully* is an
       a.   adjective.
       b.   adverb.

9. The word *ugly* is an
    a. adjective.
    b. adverb.

10. The word *slowly* is an
    a. adjective.
    b. adverb.

Quiz B   **The Writer's Resources: Adjectives/Adverbs**

Underline all the adjectives in the following sentences.

1.   That new stereo is broken.

2.   The cute little girl was a voracious reader.

3.   The storm clouds, the crackling lightening, and the horrendous thunder made for an exciting day.

4.   The torn curtain hung limply across the busted window.

5.   The classical music echoed beautifully through the hallways.

6.   Big Bob blew out the birthday candles.

7.   The earth-shattering problem was finally solved.

8.   Anthrax is deadly.

9.   The poor, cold, starving, little kitty meowed loudly at my back door.

10. The second-story window was the perfect place for a burglar to break in.

Quiz C   **The Writer's Resources: Adjectives/Adverbs**

Underline all the adverbs in the following sentences.

1.   How badly do you want dessert?

2.   I performed very poorly on the mid-term exam.

3.   Hopefully, the baseball team will win the state championship.

4.   "Surely you jest?" said the court jester.

5.   The nurse carefully applied the bandages and gently patted the patient's head.

6.   A grand piano, when played skillfully, sounds like a piece of heaven.

7.   The giant squid violently thrashed its tentacles at the quickly approaching sperm whale.

8.   The ugly duckling shook its head modestly at the reflection in the pond.

9.   "I am what I am!" exclaimed the aardvark loudly.

10.   The guitarists strummed slowly yet picked rapidly.

Quiz A   **The Writer's Resources: Clauses and Phrases**

For each of the following items, choose the best answer.

1.   A ____ is a group of related words missing a subject, a verb, or both.
   a.   clause
   b.   dependent clause
   c.   phrase
   d.   independent phrase

2.   A ____ is a group of words containing both a subject and a verb.
   a.   gerund phrase
   b.   prepositional clause
   c.   phrase
   d.   clause

3.   A phrase is always a sentence fragment.
   a.   True
   b.   False

4.   A clause is always a complete sentence.
   a.   True
   b.   False

5.   A dependent clause can stand alone as a complete sentence.
   a.   True
   b.   False

6.   All clauses are sentence fragments.
   a.   True
   b.   False

7.   A simple sentence is called
   a.   a dependent clause.
   b.   an absolute phrase.
   c.   an independent clause.
   d.   all of the above.

8.	Which of the following is not an example of the different types of commonly used phrases?
	a.	participial phrase
	b.	gerund phrase
	c.	dependent phrase
	d.	infinitive phrase
	e.	prepositional phrase

9.	Dangling modifiers are phrases or words that modify the wrong word in a sentence.
	a.	True
	b.	False

10.	Misplaced modifiers are phrases that do not seem to modify anything in the sentence, or they modify a word that makes no logical sense.
	a.	True
	b.	False

Quiz B   **The Writer's Resources: Clauses and Phrases**

In the blank, identify each group of words by writing IC for independent clause, DC for dependent clause, and P for phrase.

1. ____ Around the neighborhood streets.

2. ____ Running through the door.

3. ____ The mouse died.

4. ____ Although our taxes increased over the years.

5. ____ After you graduate from college.

6. ____ Carole ran.

7. ____ The author of <u>Writing Circles</u>.

8. ____ Their studies almost finished.

9. ____ Jumping for joy.

10. ____ Because the traffic jam lasted for hours.

Quiz C   **The Writer's Resources: Clauses and Phrases**

For each of the following sentences, underline the misplaced modifier or the dangling modifier. In the blank provided, write MM if you underlined a misplaced modifier and DM if you underlined a dangling modifier.

1. _____ Meowing incessantly, I knew it was time to feed the cat.

2. _____ Before playing the music, the cd should be cleaned.

3. _____ I nearly worked twenty hours of overtime last week.

4. _____ After rereading the book, the plot seemed very slow.

5. _____ Martin put his suit back in the closet that he had not worn.

6. _____ Somebody almost rang our doorbell a hundred times during the night.

7. _____ Failing to complete the report on time, the account was lost.

8. _____ Having too much time on his hands, the day seemed especially boring.

9. _____ I borrowed the car that ran out of gas for my blind date.

10. _____ Pulling the door closed with all my strength, the hinges broke off

Quiz A   **The Writer's Resources: Prepositions**

For each of the following items, choose the best answer.

1. A prepositional phrase contains
   a. a subject.
   b. a verb.
   c. an object.
   d. a gerund.

2. Most prepositional words indicate
   a. time and order.
   b. positions and direction.
   c. emotion and feeling.
   d. logic and reality.

3. Prepositional phrases are primarily used like adverbs and adjectives.
   a. True
   b. False

4. A prepositional phrase is a type of
   a. an independent clause.
   b. a dependent clause.
   c. a sentence fragment.
   d. none of the above.

5. You cannot begin a sentence with a prepositional phrase.
   a. True
   b. False

6. Prepositions can be linked with adjectives and verbs to create common preposition combinations in the English language.
   a. True
   b. False

7. Which of the following words is a preposition?
   a. always
   b. almost
   c. also
   d. about

8. Which of the following words is not a preposition?
    a. up
    b. through
    c. though
    d. down

9. The object of a preposition can never be a pronoun.
    a. True
    b. False

10. Prepositions can be more than one word.
    a. True
    b. False

Quiz B   **The Writer's Resources: Prepositions**

Underline the prepositional phrase in each of the following sentences.

1.   Around the corner, the thief hid the jewels.

2.   The girls skipped jumprope at the school.

3.   I worked diligently until daybreak.

4.   In spite of the weather, we sailed the boat anyway.

5.   We sailed the boat along the beach.

6.   Brynne rollerbladed from here to there.

7.   Over the next hill, the town appeared.

8.   The white rabbit disappeared into the hole.

9.   Throughout history, religion has had great political impact.

10.   During the concert, the audience danced the night away.

Quiz C   **The Writer's Resources: Prepositions**

For each of the following sentences, choose the best preposition to complete the sentence.

1.   Every weekend, we ride our bikes _____ the park.
      a.   on
      b.   into
      c.   in

2.   The giant squid lives _____ the sea.
      a.   under
      b.   down
      c.   beyond

3.   Sidewalks usually run _____ the major streets of our city.
      a.   over
      b.   across
      c.   along

4.   The insect world consists _____ many venomous insects.
      a.   from
      b.   to
      c.   of

5.   We received all of our books _____ the mail.
      a.   from
      b.   through
      c.   at

6.   _____ the play, one of the actors forgot his lines.
      a.   At
      b.   During
      c.   In

7.   _____ the lake, our cabin sits on thirty acres of forest land.
      a.   Near
      b.   With
      c.   Around

8.   _____ the bad weather, we still performed well and won the championship game.
   a.   Because of
   b.   In spite of
   c.   In regard to

9.   He flies through the air _____ the greatest of ease.
   a.   with
   b.   for
   c.   in

10.   Ben carefully walked _____ the rooftops.
   a.   through
   b.   between
   c.   upon

Quiz A   **The Writer's Resources: Capitalization**

Determine whether the following statements are true or false.

1.   Proper nouns are always capitalized.
        a.   True
        b.   False

2.   Place names are not capitalized.
        a.   True
        b.   False

3.   The days of the week are not capitalized.
        a.   True
        b.   False

4.   The first word of every sentence should always be capitalized.
        a.   True
        b.   False

5.   Proper names of people, products, and places are always capitalized.
        a.   True
        b.   False

6.   Holidays are always capitalized.
        a.   True
        b.   False

7.   Titles of books, films, and articles are always capitalized.
        a.   True
        b.   False

8.   The names of the months are capitalized.
        a.   True
        b.   False

9.   The names of the seasons are capitalized.
        a.   True
        b.   False

10.   Many times, the capitalization of words is left to the writer's discretion.
        a.   True
        b.   False

Quiz B   **The Writer's Resources: Capitalization**

For each of the following sentences, provide capitalization where it is required.

1.   i just finished reading an article in the new york times.

2.   our teacher cancelled spanish class this monday.

3.   every winter, uncle sammy opens his ski resort.

4.   brianna's birthday is august 22, but we cannot celebrate it until september.

5.   the university auditorium is under construction.

6.   "happy hanukkah!" exclaimed rabbi silverberg to the congregation.

7.   the new ford explorer is safer than last year's model.

8.   we visited many museums over spring break, but our favorite is the smithsonian museum.

9.   the chicago public library is closed on sundays.

10.   a subscription to guitar world magazine costs $19.95.

Quiz C　　　　　　　**The Writer's Resources: Capitalization**

For each of the following sentences, cross out any unnecessary capitalization.

1.　　My Uncle visits our family every Winter.

2.　　I just finished reading an editorial in <u>Time</u> Magazine.

3.　　Why does it seem like people celebrate New Year's Eve more heartily than Birthdays?

4.　　The Great Composer Beethoven is recognized by many Music Historians as simply the best.

5.　　After our Wedding Day, my Wife and I left for our Summer Honeymoon.

6.　　The City of New York is probably the most well-known City in the United States.

7.　　Cheyanna bought the new Record Album by her favorite Band, The Melting Pot.

8.　　This Fall Semester, Tia is enrolled in Accounting, English, Physics, and Spanish.

9.　　Zavier said, "I read Shakespeare's Play *The Taming of the Shrew*."

10.　Spring, Summer, Fall, and Winter are the four Seasons.

Quiz A   **The Writer's Resources: Numbers**

Determine whether the following statements are true or false.

1.   Never begin a sentence with a numerical form.
      a.   True
      b.   False

2.   Parts of a book, such as pages and chapters, always take the numerical form.
      a.   True
      b.   False

3.   Ordinarily, we can use numbers for figures above one hundred.
      a.   True
      b.   False

4.   Numbers are always used to designate dates.
      a.   True
      b.   False

5.   Although we normally write out numbers below one hundred, it is appropriate to use numbers in a passage containing several numbers.
      a.   True
      b.   False

6.   Time is always expressed in numbers.
      a.   True
      b.   False

7.   The following example is correct usage: *12 o'clock*.
      a.   True
      b.   False

8.   The following example is correct usage: *twelve P.M.*
      a.   True
      b.   False

9.   Street addresses should be written out with words rather than numbers.
      a.   True
      b.   False

10.   When writing out numbers such as 27, 66, 83, or 92, it is not necessary to use a hyphen.
       a.   True
       b.   False

Quiz B   **The Writer's Resources: Numbers**

For each of the following items, choose the best answer.

1.   Yamada has to read ____ pages for her English class tomorrow.
     a.   36
     b.   thirty-six

2.   Yamada has to read page ____ for her English class tomorrow.
     a.   36
     b.   thirty-six

3.   Vanessa's appointment is at ____ A.M.
     a.   9
     b.   nine

4.   Vanessa's appointment is at ____ o'clock in the morning.
     c.   9
     d.   nine

5.   ____ students attended the new student orientation.
     a.   212
     b.   Two hundred and twelve

6.   There are ____ hours in a day.
     a.   twenty four
     b.   twenty-four

7.   Zak hit ____ homeruns during yesterday's baseball game.
     a.   6
     b.   six

8.   Could you imagine caring for ____ dalmations?
     a.   101
     b.   one hundred and one

9.   Our new address is ____ Newberry Road.
     a.   97
     c.   ninety-seven

10. Azar was born on July ____, 1982.
     a.   1
     b.   first

Quiz C   **The Writer's Resources: Numbers**

In each blank provided, add an editing correction, or write "C" if the sentence is already correct.

1. _____ Six cows, seven chickens, and 11 pigs live on Old McDonald's Farm.

2. _____ January First is New Year's Day in North America.

3. _____ Paco always leaves for work at 7 o'clock.

4. _____ Can you help me find 1272 E. Manhattan Drive?

5. _____ I was late for class 13 times this semester.

6. _____ Tisha read 3 chapters last night.

7. _____ Tisha read chapter 3 last night.

8. _____ Macie spent fifteen dollars and seventy-two cents for a cd.

9. _____ 100 pennies is equivalent to one dollar.

10. _____ Marc plays the numbers 1, 2, 3, 4, 5, and 6 when he plays the lottery.

Quiz A   **The Writer's Resources: The Apostrophe**

Determine whether the following statements are true or false.

1.   Adding an apostrophe plus *s* to a noun indicates possession.
        a.   True
        b.   False

2.   A contraction is a combination of two words with an apostrophe representing a missing letter or letters.
        a.   True
        b.   False

3.   An apostrophe plus *s* should never be used to form plurals of figures, letters, and words in isolation.
        a.   True
        b.   False

4.   If a plural noun ends in *s*, we add an apostrophe after that *s* to show possession.
        a.   True
        b.   False

5.   A plural possessive noun ends with an apostrophe plus *s*.
        a.   True
        b.   False

6.   Should'nt is the proper contraction for *should not*.
        a.   True
        b.   False

7.   Normally, contractions should not be used in formal writing circumstances.
        a.   True
        b.   False

8.   Singular possessive nouns are formed by adding an apostrophe after the *s*.
        a.   True
        b.   False

9.   The word *boys'* is an example of a singular possessive noun.
        a.   True
        b.   False

10. The word *children's* is an example of a plural possessive noun.
    a.   True
    b.   False

Quiz B   **The Writer's Resources: Apostrophe**

Provide apostrophes for each sentence, if needed.

1.   "Why cant we come, too?" questioned Lucys cousin.

2.   Advertisings influence can have negative effects on children and adults.

3.   The Roaring Twenties was appropriately named for its lavish parties.

4.   "My aunts house isnt what youd expect," he said.

5.   Hectors New Years Eve resolution shouldve never been made.

6.   Some parents children are being home-schooled in my neighborhood.

7.   Were going to arrive after our daughters performance.

8.   My two dogs favorite food dish is the only one theyll eat from.

9.   Youre going to have to bring Marias homework home from school for her.

10.   The police officers gun was left in the criminals car.

Quiz C   **The Writer's Resources: The Apostrophe**

For each of the following nouns, form the singular (S) and the plural (P) possessive in the blanks provided.

1.   table   S_____   P_____

2.   story   S_____   P_____

3.   man   S_____   P_____

4.   home   S_____   P_____

5.   wife   S_____   P_____

6.   brother   S_____   P_____

7.   child   S_____   P_____

8.   idiot   S_____   P_____

9.   article   S_____   P_____

10. street   S_____   P_____

Instructor Comments_____

Quiz A   **The Writer's Resources: Quotation Marks**

Determine whether the following statements are true or false.

1.   Quotation marks are used to indicate when an individual is speaking.
      a.   True
      b.   False

2.   Quotation marks are not necessary to set apart written words from another source.
      a.   True
      b.   False

3.   Punctuation is always placed inside the quotation marks.
      a.   True
      b.   False

4.   Titles of books are not set apart with quotation marks.
      a.   True
      b.   False

5.   Titles of essays and articles are set apart with quotation marks.
      a.   True
      b.   False

6.   Periods and commas are placed outside the quotation marks.
      a.   True
      b.   False

7.   Single quotation marks should be used to indicate a quotation within a quotation.
      a.   True
      b.   False

8.   Semicolons and colons are placed outside the quotation marks.
      a.   True
      b.   False

9.   Do not use quotation marks to set apart your own essay title.
      a.   True
      b.   False

10.   Song titles are set apart with quotation marks.
      a.   True
      b.   False

Quiz B **The Writer's Resources: Quotation Marks**

For each of the following sentences, insert quotation marks as needed.

1.   My favorite song is Beat It, by Michael Jackson, said Julian.

2.   The word truth has puzzled philosophers for centuries.

3.   My teacher assigned the short story A sound of Thunder by Ray Bradbury.

4.   <u>Cosmopolitan</u> magazine has a worthless article entitled How to Look Like a Supermodel.

5.   I can't wait for summer, said Jade. We get to go to Disneyland.

6.   Carlisse received a B in her math class.

7.   Carlyle asked, Did the mail arrive, yet?

8.   To be or not to be; this is one of Shakespeare's most famous quotes.

9.   Is your favorite poem really called Roses are Red?

10. Many drivers fail to understand what the word yield means on a yield sign.

Quiz C   **The Writer's Resources: Quotation Marks**

In each blank provided, write "C" if the sentence is correct and "IC" if the sentence is incorrect.

1.   ____   "What happened to the puppy dog's ear"? asked the little girl.

2.   ____   I just read the book "The Gate to Women's Country."

3.   ____   Our class is supposed to use the article "You Can't Define Gender" for our research analysis.

4.   ____   "The word god" means many different things to many different people.

5.   ____   The woman exclaimed, "Watch out for that car!"

6.   ____   In his short story "Alien Colors", Herman Mattok explores how humans visualize their world.

7.   ____   "Call me Ishmael." The famous line in <u>Moby Dick</u> provokes quite a character sketch.

8.   ____   "Call me Bob" just doesn't have the same impact.

9.   ____   "Yes," replied the professor. "You have to write a book."

10. ____   "One o'clock, two o'clock, three o'clock rock" is how the song <u>Rock Around the Clock</u> begins.

Quiz A   **The Writer's Resources: Parentheses, Brackets, The Dash, and The Hyphen**

For each of the following sentences, choose the best answer.

1.   ____ are used to join descriptive adjectives before a noun.
   a.   Hyphens
   b.   Dashes
   c.   Parentheses
   d.   Brackets

2.   We use ____ to set off additional information, explanations, or qualifications of the main idea in a sentence.
   a.   hyphens
   b.   dashes
   c.   parentheses
   d.   brackets

3.   The ____ is used to set apart material that needs more emphasis than would be indicated by parentheses.
   a.   hyphen
   b.   dash
   c.   bracket

4.   To set apart editorial explanations in quoted material, we use ____.
   a.   hyphens
   b.   dashes
   c.   parentheses
   d.   brackets

5.   ____ are used to create many compound words.
   a.   Hyphens
   b.   Dashes
   c.   Parentheses
   d.   Brackets

6.   We often use ____ to set apart dates.
   a.   hyphens
   b.   dashes
   c.   parentheses
   d.   brackets

7. Periods will always be placed after parentheses.
   a. True
   b. False

8. Dashes can be used to combine words together.
   a. True
   b. False

9. Never combine with a hyphen an adjective that ends in *-ly* with another adjective.
   a. True
   b. False

10. Normally, the word "sic" (meaning "thus") is placed within _____ to indicate an error within a direct quote.
    a. hyphens
    b. dashes
    c. parentheses
    d. brackets

Quiz B   **The Writer's Resources: Parentheses, Brackets, The Dash, and The Hyphen**

For each of the following sentences, use an "X" or "Xs" to indicate the appropriate place in the sentence where the indicated punctuation would go.

1.   (parentheses)   The Civil War 1861-1865 between the North and South still has ramifications today.

2.   (dash)   My favorite employee there she is now just had her first baby girl.

3.   (hyphen)   The white gloved server tripped over the wine stained, torn carpet.

4.   (hyphen)   The sonic boom created by the Air Force jets was literally window shattering.

5.   (brackets)   The campaign sign read Just Say Know sic to Drugs.

6.   (parentheses)   The final product should be tasty as well as eye-catching see photo on page 332.

7.   (dash)   Louise desired only one thing in her life love.

8.   (dash)   The students lined up outside the classroom doors as they did every morning alphabetically.

9.   (hyphen)   We all have to make self sacrifices when it comes to an all encompassing education.

10.   (parentheses)   The IRS Internal Revenue Service is always unpopular during April.

Quiz C   **The Writer's Resources: Parentheses, Brackets, The Dash, and The Hyphen**

In each blank provided, write "C" if the sentence is correct and "IC" if the sentence is incorrect.

1. _____ Harold, my good-for-nothing brother-in-law asked if he could stay at our house

2. _____ We—my mother, sister, and I—always get together to celebrate Oktoberfest.

3. _____ The enchilada recipe (page 52) is just not spicy enough for my taste.

4. _____ The president-elect's letter states, "If you vote for me, I will strongly suport [sic] education."

5. _____ The anti trust clause caused too many grievances.

6. _____ The hogs went hog-wild after the earth shattering earthquake.

7. _____ The nine month old baby seemed to favor a specific color—yellow.

8. _____ The judge could not condone such a punishment in his court (even though he agreed with it).

9. _____ For-the-record, Gus did not sign the contract in the right spot.

10. _____ We enjoy a well-written sitcom—especially after coffee and dessert—during our weekday evenings.

Quiz A   **The Writer's Resources: Commonly Misspelled Words**

Circle the correctly spelled word in each of the following pairs.

1.   grammar   grammer

2.   rhythm   rhythem

3.   ridiculus   ridiculous

4.   seperate   separate

5.   since   sinse

6.   surprise   suprise

7.   paticular   particular

8.   thorough   thourogh

9.   probly   probably

10. calendar   calender

11. personnel   personell

12. maintain   maintane

13. across   accross

14. carear   career

15. environment   enviroment

16. desparate   desperate

17. embarrass   embarass

18. finelly   finally

19. interest   intrest

20. interfear   interfere

Quiz B   **The Writer's Resources: Commonly Misspelled Words**

For each of the following sentences, provide the correct spelling of the hyphenated word in the blank provided.

1.   When Guillan said no, he m-e-n-t _____ "No!"

2.   It is n-e-s-s-r-y _____ to eat every four hours.

3.   Most people get n-r-v-u-s _____ when they speak in public.

4.   Recent studies show that many Americans are above average w-e-t _____.

5.   Tiger Woods is a very famous a-t-h-l-t _____.

6.   I always have a guilty c-n-s-n-c-e _____ when I have two helpings of dessert.

7.   My mother d-s-a-p-r-v-s _____ of me staying out past midnight.

8.   Yesterday, one of my classmates got into an a-r-g-u-m-t _____ with our teacher.

9.   An o-p-t-m-s-t _____ views the glass as half full.

10. B-e-g-n-i-n-g _____ today, I have to get up earlier.

Name_____ Instructor_____

Date_____ Score_____

Instructor Comments_____

Quiz C   **The Writer's Resources: Commonly Misspelled Words**

In the blank provided, write the correct version of the misspelled word.

1. adress   _____

2. heighth   _____

3. privledge   _____

4. ilegal   _____

5. untill   _____

6. judgement   _____

7. jewlry   _____

8. familir   _____

9. opinnion   _____

10. purform   _____

11. sucsess   _____

12. persue   _____

13. refrence   _____

14. preffer   _____

15. possable   _____

16. occassion   _____

17. diferrent   _____

18. behaviur   _____

19. prejudise   _____

20. imediately   _____

Name_____   Instructor_____

Date_____   Score_____

Instructor Comments_____

Quiz A   **The Writer's Resources: Words that Sound Alike**

For each of the following words, write the word which sounds alike in the blank provided.

1.   buy   _____

2.   capitol   _____

3.   your   _____

4.   plane   _____

5.   cite   _____

6.   too   _____

7.   reign   _____

8.   past   _____

9.   aural   _____

10. compliment   _____

11. presents   _____

12. whole   _____

13. threw   _____

14. weather   _____

15. write   _____

16. waist   _____

17. its   _____

18. principle   _____

19. whose   _____

20. there   _____

Quiz B   **The Writer's Resources: Words that Sound Alike**

Underline the correct word for each of the following sentences.

1.   (It's, Its) a myth that butter helps skin burns.

2.   Our elementary school could use a new (principle, principal).

3.   The (principle, principal) idea is one of utilitarianism.

4.   Be sure to (site, cite) all direct quotes in a research essay.

5.   (Weather, Whether) or not we make it on time depends on the traffic.

6.   Many psychologists believe that murderers have no (conscience, conscious).

7.   Most people do not believe that we have all had (passed, past) lives.

8.   "Take a deep (breath, breathe)," said the swim coach.

9.   Mazar said, " I (except, accept) your apology."

10.   Television violence has a detrimental (affect, effect) on children.

Quiz C   **The Writer's Resources: Words that Sound Alike**

Underline the correct word for each of the following sentences.

1.   The (consul, council) from China gave an impassioned speech

2.   My mother always told us, "No (dessert, desert) if you do not eat all of your vegetables."

3.   Husbands tend to (loose, lose) the car keys more than wives.

4.   Our (personal, personnel) office needs to hire a new director.

5.   We read Dear Abby's (advice, advise) column every Sunday.

6.   (They're, Their) late for every dinner reservation.

7.   (Their, There) does Shantile on another research mission.

8.   (Where, Were) are we now?

9.   "Excuse me," said the worker, "(You're, Your) in my way."

10.   The Grapes of Wrath is assigned more often (than, then) Frankenstein.

Quiz A   **The Writer's Resources: Two- and Three-Word Verb Phrases**

In the blank provided, insert the proper preposition to create a phrasal verb to complete the sentence.

1.   Nationwide studies suggest that too many students drop _____ of highschool.

2.   Professor Goldstein pointed _____ the illogical statement.

3.   It is my job to call _____ all of my old classmates to inform them about the reunion.

4.   My boss accidentally handed _____ the account figures late.

5.   Most editors will cross _____ errors on a first draft.

6.   When people pass _____ from old age, it is simply the cycle of life.

7.   I can never figure _____ the extra-credit problems on the math exams

8.   It is wise to look _____ your shoulder when walking down a dark alley.

9.   My parents always bring _____ my mischievous behavior.

10.   When mom goes to work, I have to look _____ my little sister.

Quiz B   **The Writer's Resources: Two- and Three-Word Verb Phrases**

In the blank provided, write "C" if the sentence is correct or "IC" if the sentence is incorrect.

1. ____   Jefferson Jr. is named after his father.

2. ____   Elementary school teachers have to put on with a lot of class disruptions.

3. ____   Diego and his spouse turn in very early in the evening.

4. ____   My coach always said, "Never give out. You can still win."

5. ____   I hang out my clothes in the closet before bed every night.

6. ____   The volunteer did not fill up the questionnaire properly.

7. ____   It is awkward when you have to kick a student out of class.

8. ____   You need a school I.D. card when you check up a book from the library.

9. ____   Doctors say it takes nine days to get over a common cold.

10. ____   Clem handed his homework in late.

Quiz C   **The Writer's Resources: Two- and Three-Word Verb Phrases**

Circle the correct phrasal verb for each sentence.

1.   We (pass out, pass in) block-watch pamphlets in our neighborhood once a month.

2.   My accountant (goes over, goes around) all of my tax forms before I send them in.

3.   The city will (tear up, tear down) the old school before building the new one.

4.   Margaret and Danielle (put back, put off) their weekend chores until Sunday night.

5.   The kids on my block decided to (take off, take over) the treehouse on the next street.

6.   We are so busy that we have to (turn down, turn over) new contracts.

7.   I am a genius when it comes to (making up, making out) excuses.

8.   (Picking out, Picking up) fresh, tasty produce at the grocery store takes time and skill.

9.   My husband forgets to (shut off, shut out) the porch light every morning.

10.   Private detectives (look in, look into) sensitive matters for the public.

MIDTERM EXAM

For each of the following items, choose the best answer.

1.   The thesis sentence
      a.   has only one topic, never more.
      b.   does not express topic as a fact.
      c.   can outline the organizational structure of the essay.
      d.   all of the above

2.   The purpose of an introductory sentence is to
      a.   catch the reader's attention and clarify the author's tone.
      b.   introduce the main topic and the author's opinion.
      c.   start the essay with a thesis.

3.   Words like is/is not and should/should not are examples of verbs that begin to tell the reader how the author feels about the topic.
      a.   True
      b.   False

4.   The thesis sentence is an example of a three-item essay map:
      Everyone should carpool because it saves gas and decreases pollution.
      a.   True
      b.   False

5.   Support sentences help develop the subject by using
      a.   specific facts, examples, and tone.
      b.   specific facts, statistics, and details.
      c.   specific facts, details, and examples.

6.   A working outline is used to
      a.   discover whether or not you have a good working essay map.
      b.   discover whether or not you have a topic, controlling idea/attitude, and support.
      c.   discover whether or not you have good organization.

7.   A concluding paragraph
      a.   brings a sense of completion to the essay.
      b.   brings a sense of completion to the essay and restates the central thesis.
      c.   brings a sense of completion to the essay and re-emphasises the central thesis.

8. Summarizing and judging in a concluding paragraph is
   a. an evaluation
   b. a warning.
   c. a prediction.
   d. none of the above

9. Call or write to the March of Dimes, and suggest they use more funding to help provide better prenatal care for pregnant women.
   a. prediction
   b. warning
   c. call to action
   d. evaluation

10. Set some money aside as soon as possible, and begin investing for the future.
    a. prediction
    b. warning
    c. call to action
    d. evaluation

11. The question "Is the subject impossible?" is an example of circumstance in
    a. listing.
    b. mapping.
    c. cubing.
    d. cross-examination.
    e. any of the above techniques.

12. Four strategies to help a writer get started are listing, clustering, cubing, and mapping.
    a. True
    b. False

13. In a concluding paragraph for a descriptive essay, _____ is often used as the approach.
    a. dominant impression
    b. symbolism
    c. evaluation
    d. none of the above

14. Which of the following are included in the six perspectives of the cubing strategy?
    a. Free associate about the topic.
    a. Apply the topic.
    b. Organize the topic.
    c. a and c
    d. a and b

15. The two different types of description are
    a. objective and illustrative.
    b. illustrative and emotional.
    c. objective and subjective.
    d. emotional and subjective.

16. In a concluding paragraph for a descriptive essay, _____ is often used as the approach.
    a. dominant impression
    b. symbolism
    c. evaluation
    d. none of the above

17. The easiest way to develop a narrative is to rely on the six reporter's questions: *who, what, where, when, why,* and *how.*
    a. True
    b. False

18. In a narrative essay, the thesis should
    a. state the point of the story.
    b. lay out the essay map.
    c. both a and b
    d. none of the above

19. Which of the following is not a good transition to use in an example essay?
    a. for instance
    b. to illustrate
    c. specifically
    d. generally

20. The six reporter's questions have no relevance when writing an example essay.
    a. True
    b. False

21. Detailed examples in an example essay are developed in the _____ paragraph(s).
    a. introductory
    b. body
    c. conclusion

22. A classification essay thesis statement should contain
    a. the writer's controlling idea.
    b. the word *classification.*
    c. the method of how the author picked the topic.
    d. none of the above.

23. The most important aspect of classification is to keep the classifying units the same.
   a. True
   b. False

24. If we were to classify instruments, which category or sub-unit does not apply to our method of division?
   a. wind instruments
   b. string instruments
   c. percussion instrument
   d. electric instruments

25. In a classification essay, each _____ paragraph expands on one of the categories.
   a. introductory
   b. topic
   c. transitional
   d. body

FINAL EXAM

For each of the following items, choose the best answer.

1.   A process essay explains the steps necessary to complete
       a.   a procedure.
       b.   an operation.
       c.   an event.
       d.   all of the above.

2.   The two types of process essays are
       a.   informational and substantial.
       b.   directional and substantial.
       c.   substantial and insubstantial.
       d.   directional and informational.

3.   Directional and informational process essays should begin with a thesis statement that
       a.   announces the topic.
       b.   expresses the writer's controlling idea.
       c.   contains an essay map.
       d.   all of the above.

4.   Comparison and contrast writing focuses on a discussion of an object, idea, or item in terms of how it relates to its own features.
       a.   True
       b.   False

5.   A comparison and contrast thesis statement must contain
       a.   the items to be compared or contrasted.
       b.   the controlling idea or attitude.
       c.   the organizational structure.
       d.   all of the above.

6.   Which of the following organizational plans presents information about one item first, then refers to this information when discussing the second item?
       a.   block method
       b.   point-by-point method
       c.   series-by-series method
       d.   diagram method

7.	Definition by negation begins by stating what a word or term
	a.	opposes.
	b.	demonstrates.
	c.	is not.
	d.	none of the above

8.	In a definition essay, the thesis statement should
	a.	state the topic to be defined.
	b.	state an attitude toward the topic.
	c.	stress the main points that will be made.
	d.	all of the above

8.	Appropriate transitional expressions for developing a definition essay are unnecessary because definition writing uses any and all rhetorical modes of development.
	a.	True
	b.	False

9.	Cause and effect essays analyze
	a.	special relationships.
	b.	casual relationships.
	c.	causal relationships.
	d.	hierarchical relationships.

10.	In a cause or effect essay, the thesis statement should
	a.	demonstrate order.
	b.	indicate action.
	c.	be causal and effective.
	d.	none of the above

11.	Which of the following transitional expressions does not suggest causes?
	a.	since
	b.	the reason
	c.	consequently
	d.	because

12.	When writing a persuasive essay, it is only necessary to know the major argumentative points concerning your side of the argument.
	a.	True
	b.	False

13.	Which of the following is not considered a valid type of support used to convince readers?
	a.	predicting causes
	b.	answering the opposition
	c.	referring to authority
	d.	facts and examples

14. A thesis statement in a persuasion essay should contain the writer's conclusion or point of view concerning the topic.
    a.   True
    b.   False

15. The research paper can be considered as an extended essay.
    a.   True
    b.   False

16. What kind of material should you look for to support your ideas and conclusions for a research essay?
    a.   appeals to emotion
    b.   appeals to reason
    c.   appeals to the opposition
    d.   none of the above

17. All research papers must include a Works Cited page.
    a.   True
    b.   False

18. Failure to document the use of another's ideas, even if you put it in your words, is called
    _____.
    a.   misquoting
    b.   summarizing
    c.   plagiarism
    d.   none of the above

19. Essay questions are called
    a.   terms.
    b.   responses.
    c.   modes.
    d.   prompts.

20. Helping you figure out how to respond to the essay question is best illustrated by the
    a.   key term(s).
    b.   topic.
    c.   attitude.
    d.   none of the above

21. Essay exams usually involve the challenge of relying on your memory for ideas and facts.
    a.   True
    b.   False

22. A work of criticism involves interpreting and evaluating your own work.
    a.   True
    b.   False

23. Cultural qualities of a setting in a piece of literature include which of the following? (Circle all that apply.)
    a. moral
    b. community
    c. social
    d. political

24. Generally, a theme should be a moral, a commandment, or a directive about how to live.
    a. True
    b. False

25. The point of view in a piece of literature refers to who is telling the story.
    a. True
    b. False

ANSWER KEY

Chapter 3 Test A
1.	e	6.	b
2.	b	7.	c
3.	d	8.	a
4.	d	9.	d
5.	a	10.	b

Chapter 3 Test B
1.	a	6.	a
2.	b	7.	b
3.	a	8.	b
4.	b	9.	a
5.	b	10.	b

Chapter 4 Test A
1.	d	6.	b
2.	a	7.	b
3.	c	8.	b
4.	b	9.	b
5.	b	10.	b

Chapter 4 Test B
1. T, S
2. S, T
3. S, T
4. T, S
5. T, S

Chapter 5 Test A
1.	c	6.	a
2.	b	7.	b
3.	a	8.	b
4.	call to	9.	a
	action,	10.	c
	warning,		
	prediction,		
	evaluation		
5.	b		

Chapter 5 Test B
1.	b	6.	b
2.	c	7.	c
3.	a	8.	a
4.	d	9.	b
5.	d	10.	c

Chapter 6 Test A
1.	b	6.	a
2.	a	7.	b
3.	a	8.	a
4.	a	9.	a
5.	b	10.	a

Chapter 6 Test B
1.	b	6.	a
2.	d	7.	d
3.	a	8.	e
4.	d	9.	b
5.	e	10.	b

Chapter 7 Test A
1.	a	6.	c
2.	a	7.	a
3.	c	8.	b
4.	a	9.	b
5.	d	10.	d

Chapter 7 Test B
1-10 Answers vary.

Chapter 8 Test A
1.	b	6.	b
2.	b	7.	a
3.	a	8.	c
4.	c	9.	b
5.	a	10.	a

Chapter 8 Test B
1-10 Answers vary.

Chapter 9 Test A
1.	b	6.	d
2.	c	7.	b
3.	a	8.	a
4.	c	9.	c
5.	a	10.	b

Chapter 9 Test B
1-10 Answers vary.

Chapter 10 Test A
1.	a	6.	b
2.	a	7.	a
3.	b	8.	b
4.	a	9.	d
5.	c	10.	d

Chapter 10 Test B
1-10 Answers vary.

Chapter 11 Test A
1.	d	6.	a
2.	b	7.	a
3.	a	8.	a
4.	d	9.	b
5.	b	10.	d

Chapter 11 Test B
1. D
2. I
3. I
4. D
5. I

Chapter 12 Test A
1.	b	6.	c
2.	a	7.	a
3.	d	8.	b
4.	a	9.	c
5.	b	10.	d

Chapter 12 Test B
1-10 Answers vary.

Chapter 13 Test A
1.	c	6.	a
2.	c	7.	a
3.	b	8.	b
4.	c	9.	c
5.	d	10.	b

Chapter 13 Test B
1-10 Answers vary.

Chapter 14 Test A
1.	c	6.	c
2.	a	7.	c
3.	b	8.	d
4.	a	9.	d
5.	c	10.	a

Chapter 14 Test B
1-10 Answers vary.

ANSWER KEY

Chapter 15 Test A
1. b   6. b
2. b   7. a
3. a   8. a, c, d
4. a   9. a
5. a   10. a

Chapter 15 Test B
1. either-or
2. hasty generalization
3. bandwagon
4. bandwagon
5. adhomonym
6. red herring
7. nonsequitur
8. nonsequitur
9. ad homonym
10. red herring

Chapter 16 Test A
1. a   6. b
2. b   7. b
3. d   8. a
4. b   9. a
5. b   10. c

Chapter 16 Test B
1. 7   6. 8
2. 4   7. 2
3. 1   8. 5
4. 3   9. 9
5. 10   10. 6

Chapter 17 Test A
1. b   6. b
2. a   7. c
3. d   8. b
4. a   9. a
5. b   10. a

Chapter 17 Test B
1. Discuss
2. Explain, define
3. Summarize
4. causes
5. Compare, contrast
6. Evaluate
7. classify
8. Analyze
9. Describe, effects
10. effects, Discuss, illustrations

Chapter 18 Test A
1. b   6. b
2. c   7. d
3. a, c, d   8. a
4. b   9. a
5. a   10. a

Chapter 18 Test B
1. c   6. b
2. a   7. b
3. b   8. a
4. c   9. c
5. a   10. a

ANSWER KEY for WRITER'S RESOURCES

Nouns/Pronouns
Quiz A
1. c   6. a
2. c   7. a
3. a   8. a
4. a   9. c
5. c   10. a

Nouns/Pronouns
Quiz B
1. d   6. c
2. c   7. a
3. a   8. b
4. a   9. c
5. b   10. a

Nouns/Pronouns
Quiz C
1. Georgio, his, brother, school
2. Each, exam
3. Anybody, who
4. Maria, gift, her
5. His, computer, monitor
6. We, it, ourselves
7. Who, dinner, tonight
8. She, it, him
9. That
10. You, yourself, others

Verbs Quiz A
1. d   6. a
2. c   7. b
3. b   8. b
4. c   9. a
5. a   10. b

Verbs   Quiz B
1. climb
2. think, am
3. will be skating
4. has shopped
5. crashed, slid
6. hates, loves
7. bit
8. was bitten
9. has been studying
10. lies

Verbs   Quiz C
1. go   6. is
2. comes   7. are
3. looks   8. plays
4. is   9. has
5. bake   10. sits

Adjectives/Adverbs
Quiz A
1. d   6. b
2. d   7. a
3. b   8. b
4. a   9. a
5. b   10. b

Adjectives/Adverbs
Quiz B
1. new, broken
2. cute, little, voracious
3. storm, crackling horrendous, exciting
4. torn, busted
5. classical
6. Big, birthday
7. earth-shattering
8. deadly
9. poor, cold, starving, little, back
10. second-story, perfect

Adjectives/Adverbs
Quiz C
1. badly
2. poorly
3. Hopefully
4. Surely
5. carefully, gently
6. skillfully
7. violently, quickly
8. modestly
9. loudly
10. slowly, rapidly

Clauses/Phrases
Quiz A
1. c   6. b
2. d   7. c
3. a   8. c
4. b   9. b
5. b   10. b

Clauses/Phrases
Quiz B
1. P   6. IC
2. P   7. P
3. IC   8. P
4. DC   9. P
5. DC   10. DC

Clauses/Phrases
Quiz C
1. MM   6. MM
2. DM   7. DM
3. MM   8. DM
4. DM   9. MM
5. MM   10. DM

ANSWER KEY for WRITER'S RESOURCES

Prepositions
Quiz A
1. c   6. a
2. b   7. d
3. a   8. c
4. c   9. b
5. b   10. a

Prepositions
Quiz B
1. Around the corner
2. at the school
3. until daybreak
4. In spite of the weather
5. along the beach
6. from here to there
7. Over the next hill
8. into the hole
9. Throughout history
10. During the concert

Preposition
Quiz C
1. c   6. b
2. a   7. a
3. c   8. b
4. c   9. a
5. b   10. c

Capitalization
Quiz A
1. a   6. a
2. b   7. a
3. b   8. a
4. a   9. b
5. a   10. b

Capitalization
Quiz B
1. I, New York Times
2. Our, Spanish, Monday
3. Every, Uncle, Sammy
4. Brianna's, August, September
5. The
6. Happy Hanukkah, Rabbi, Silverberg
7. The, Ford, Explorer
8. We, Smithsonian Museum
9. The Chicago Public Library, Sundays
10. A, Guitar World

Capitalization
Quiz C
1. uncle, winter
2. magazine
3. birthdays
4. great, composer, music, historians
5. wedding day, wife summer, honeymoon
6. city, city
7. record, album, band
8. fall, semester accounting, physics
9. play
10. summer, fall, winter, seasons

Numbers
Quiz A
1. a   6. b
2. a   7. b
3. a   8. b
4. a   9. b
5. a   10. b

Numbers
Quiz B
1. b   6. b
2. a   7. b
3. a   8. a
4. b   9. a
5. b   10. a

Numbers
Quiz C
1. eleven
2. 1
3. seven
4. C
5. thirteen
6. three
7. C
8. $15.72
9. One hundred
10. C

Apostrophe
Quiz A
1. a   6. b
2. a   7. a
3. b   8. b
4. a   9. b
5. b   10. a

Apostrophe
Quiz B
1. can't, Lucy's
2. Advertising's
3. no apostrophe
4. aunt's, isn't, you'd
5. Hector's, Year's, should've
6. parents'
7. We're, daughter's
8. dogs', they'll
9. You're, Maria's
10. officer's, criminal's

Apostrophe
Quiz C
1. table's, tables'
2. story's, stories'
3. man's, men's
4. home's, homes'
5. wife's, wives'
6. brother's, brothers'
7. child's, children's
8. idiot's, idiots'
9. article's, articles'
10. street's, streets'

ANSWER KEY for WRITER'S RESOURCES

Quotation Marks
Quiz A

1.	a	6.	b
2.	b	7.	a
3.	b	8.	a
4.	a	9.	a
5.	a	10.	a

Parentheses, Brackets, Dash, Hyphen   Quiz A

1.	a	6.	d
2.	c	7.	b
3.	b	8.	b
4.	d	9.	a
5.	a	10.	d

Commonly Misspelled Words
Quiz A

1.	grammar	11.	personnel
2.	rhythm	12.	maintain
3.	ridiculous	13.	across
4.	separate	14.	career
5.	since	15.	environment
6.	surprise	16.	desperate
7.	particular	17.	embarrass
8.	thorough	18.	finally
9.	probably	19.	interest
10.	calendar	20	interfere

Quotation Marks
Quiz B

See Attachment 1

Parentheses, Brackets, Dash, Hyphen   Quiz B

See Attachment 2

Commonly Misspelled Words
Quiz B

1. meant
2. necessary
3. nervous
4. weight
5. athlete
6. conscience
7. disapproves
8. argument
9. optimist
10. Beginning

Quotation Marks
Quiz C

1.	IC	6.	IC
2.	IC	7.	C
3.	C	8.	C
4.	IC	9.	C
5.	C	10.	IC

Parentheses, Brackets, Dash, Hyphen   Quiz C

1.	IC	6.	IC
2.	C	7.	IC
3.	C	8.	C
4.	C	9.	IC
5.	IC	10.	C

Commonly Misspelled Words
Quiz C

1.	address	11.	success
2.	height	12.	pursue
3.	privilege	13.	reference
4.	illegal	14.	prefer
5.	until	15.	possible
6.	judgment	16.	occasion
7.	jewelry	17.	different
8.	familiar	18.	behavior
9.	opinion	19.	prejudice
10.	perform	20.	immediately

ANSWER KEY for WRITER'S RESOURCES

Words that Sound Alike
Quiz A

1. by
2. capital
3. you're
4. plain
5. sight/site
6. two/to
7. rain/rein
8. passed
9. oral
10. complement
11. presence
12. hole
13. through
14. whether
15. right/rite
16. waste
17. it's
18. principal
19. who's
20. their/they're

Two- and Three-Word Verb Phrases
Quiz A

1. out
2. out
3. up
4. in
5. out
6. away
7. out
8. over
9. up
10. after

Words that Sound Alike
Quiz B

1. It's
2. principal
3. principle
4. cite
5. Whether
6. conscience
7. past
8. breath
9. accept
10. effect

Two- and Three-Word Verb Phrases
Quiz B

1. C
2. IC
3. C
4. IC
5. IC
6. IC
7. C
8. IC
9. C
10. C

Words that Sound Alike
Quiz C

1. consul
2. dessert
3. lose
4. personnel
5. advice
6. They're
7. There
8. Where
9. You're
10. than

Two- and Three-Word Verb Phrases
Quiz C

1. pass out
2. goes over
3. tear down
4. put off
5. take over
6. turn down
7. making up
8. Picking out
9. shut off
10. look into

ANSWER KEY

MID TERM EXAM	FINAL EXAM
1. d	1. d
2. a	2. d
3. a	3. d
4. b	4. b
5. c	5. d
6. c	6. a
7. c	7. c
8. a	8. b
9. c	9. c
10. c	10. c
11. d	11. c
12. a	12. b
13. c	13. b
14. c	14. a
15. c	15. a
16. c	16. b
17. a	17. a
18. c	18. c
19. d	19. d
20. b	20. d
21. b	21. a
22. a	22. b
23. a	23. a, c, d
24. d	24. b
25. d	25. a

Attachment 1

Quiz B   **The Writer's Resources: Quotation Marks**

1.   "My favorite song is 'Beat It,' by Michael Jackson," said Julian.

2.   The word "truth" has puzzled philosophers for centuries.

3.   My teacher assigned the short story "A sound of Thunder" by Ray Bradbury.

4.   <u>Cosmopolitan</u> magazine has a worthless article entitled "How to Look Like a Supermodel."

5.   "I can't wait for summer," said Jade. "We get to go to Disneyland."

6.   Carlisse received a "B" in her math class.

7.   Carlyle asked, "Did the mail arrive, yet?"

8.   "To be or not to be"; this is one of Shakespeare's most famous quotes.

9.   Is your favorite poem really called "Roses are Red"?

10.   Many drivers fail to understand what the word "yield" means on a yield sign.

Quiz B   **The Writer's Resources: Parentheses, Brackets, The Dash, and**
The Hyphen

1.   (parentheses) The Civil War (1861-1865) between the North and South still has
              ramifications today.

2.   (dash)   My favorite employee—there she is now—just had her first baby girl.

3.   (hyphen)   The white-gloved server tripped over the wine-stained, torn carpet.

4.   (hyphen)   The sonic boom created by the Air Force jets was literally
              window-shattering.

5.   (brackets)   The campaign sign read Just Say Know [sic] to Drugs.

6.   (parentheses) The final product should be tasty as well as eye-catching (see photo on
              page 332).

7.   (dash)   Louise desired only one thing in her life—love.

8.   (dash)   The students lined up outside the classroom doors as they did every
              morning—alphabetically.

9.   (hyphen)   We all have to make self-sacrifices when it comes to an all-encompassing
              education.

10.   (parentheses) The IRS (Internal Revenue Service) is always unpopular during April.